Algrove Publishing Limited
36 Mill Street
Almonte, Ontario
Canada K0A 1A0

Telephone: (613) 256-0350
Fax: (613) 256-0360
Email: sales@algrove.com

National Library of Canada Cataloguing in Publication

Williams, J. R. (James Robert), 1888-1957.
    The Bull of the Woods II / J.R. Williams.

(Classic reprint series)
ISBN 1-894572-81-5

      1. American wit and humor, Pictorial. 2. Machinists--Caricatures and cartoons. 3. Machine shops--Caricatures and cartoons. I. Title. II. Series: Classic reprint series (Almonte, Ont.)

NC1429.W573A4 2003   741.5'973   C2003-904746-6

Printed in Canada
#10703

Publisher's Note

James Robert Williams was born in Nova Scotia in 1888. He ran away from home in his mid-teens, worked on a ranch for a while, then spent three years with the U.S. Cavalry. After he married, he took a full-time job with a crane manufacturing company in Ohio. He became a full-time cartoonist in 1921, continuing to draw *Out Our Way* and other series until his death in 1957.

Leonard G. Lee, Publisher
Almonte, Ontario
July 2003

Foreword

The term "Bull of the Woods" was borrowed from the lumber-jacks. I used it to describe a gruff, poker-faced man prowling among hundreds of machine belts in a shop in Alliance, Ohio. Silhouetted against the hazy shop windows, they had a certain resemblance to a dense woods.

The "Bull" was hardboiled, perhaps, but he was kind. He must have been, or I certainly should have been fired. He said to me one day with fine sarcasm, "Pardon my rudeness. You've been turning out two cartoons and one shaft a day on this machine. Couldn't you make it two shafts and one cartoon a day? This is a machine shop."

And now, when I have no shafts to do, I have a terrible time turning out one cartoon a day.

J. R. Williams

GOING UP.

2

THE CORONER'S JURY.

4

HEROES ARE MADE - NOT BORN

THE HAPPY MEDIUM.

6

"THE BIG LOAFER."

THE POOR RICH GUY.

THE CROWDED MOMENT.

9

THE NOSE WARMER

THE TIME KILLER

J.R.WILLIAMS

THE OLD FASHIONED SHOVEL.

SAY UNCLE!

THE SCOOP

J.R.WILLIAMS

14

THE REPRIEVE.

J.R.WILLIAMS

THE TAKE OFF

J.R.WILLIAMS

THE FLY IN THE SALVE.

J.R.WILLIAMS

WHY MOTHERS GET GRAY.

THE SPEEDERS.

MANS INHUMANITY TO MAN

DENTING A HIGH-HAT.

23

THE STRONG MIND.

THE CONVENIENCE.

"THE HARE AND THE TURTLE.

J.R.WILLIAMS

THE STORY WITHOUT AN END.

J.P. WILLIAMS

THE SECOND FIDDLE.

J.R.WILLIAMS

SEATING CAPACITY.

J.R.WILLIAMS

29

BRAIN FOG.

WHERE THE MINORITY WINS

THE FLOATER

J.R.WILLIAMS

GOOD LOOKIN'

J.R.WILLIAMS

THE FORGETTER

J.R.WILLIAMS

THE SOFT SPOT.

35

THE RUSH HOUR

J.R. WILLIAMS

INSTINCTIVELY SPEAKING.

J.R.WILLIAMS

GREEK

J.R.WILLIAMS

38

HEROES ARE MADE—NOT BORN.

J.R.WILLIAMS

WHY MOTHERS GET GRAY
THE SMUGGLER.

J.P.WILLIAMS

THE NIGHT BIRD

J.R.WILLIAMS

"THE BULL O' TH' WOODS"

J.P. WILLIAMS

A CONTINUED STORY.

JOHNNIE BULL AND THE BULL.

44

THE WHISTLE RUSHER.

J.R.WILLIAMS

THE GENTLEMEN.

A FITTING FIT.

J.R.WILLIAMS

47

THE METAL WORKER.

J.R.WILLIAMS

48

SLEEPING SLICKNESS

THE BEGINNER.

SNAPPING OUT OF IT.

THE LAMB

J.P.WILLIAMS

"WHEN DAY IS DONE"

J.R.WILLIAMS

55

OUT OF THE DUSK.

STILL LIFE.

EVERYTHING'S LOOKING UP.

J.R.WILLIAMS

SILENCE IS GOLDEN

THE INNOCENT BYSTANDER

THE SMART SET.

J.R.WILLIAMS

61

THE "HOT" SPOT.

WE'RE ALL DOIN' TH' SAME

TWO MISTAKES.

J.R.WILLIAMS

THE SOFT SPOT.

J. R. WILLIAMS

SO NEAR, AND YET SO FAR.

THE "NO" BODY.

J.R.Williams

67

THE FEMININE TOUCH

OPPORTUNITY KNOCKS.

69

A TIME FOR EVERYTHING

THE NUT.

J.R.WILLIAMS

THE RUN-OUT.

THE TEACHER.

J.R.WILLIAMS

73

BLISS.

J.R.WILLIAMS

THE SEE LION

BORN THIRTY YEARS TOO SOON.

THE STAY-AT-HOME

THE HOLD-UP.

J.R.WILLIAMS

THE PASSING STORM.

J.R.WILLIAMS

HUMPTY DUMPTIES

J.R.WILLIAMS

MACHINE AGED.

81

A FOLLOWING

INS AND OUTS.

THE LAST MILE

THE NEWS HOUND.

THE TWO THINKERS.

NAPOLEON AND THE ALPS.

BURIED IN THOUGHT.

SUCCESS?

J.R.WILLIAMS

A FREE FEED

J.R.WILLIAMS

THE THINKER.

J.R.WILLIAMS

THE GRAY BEARDS

THE NEW ERA.

J.R.WILLIAMS

SUSPENDED ANIMATION.

J.R.WILLIAMS

THE GOAT.

ART.

97

BACK SEAT GENIUS.

THE NEW ERA

J.R.WILLIAMS

99

LOVE THAT SOON DIES

100

THE GRAND OLD RAG.

101

INCONVENIENT CONVENIENCES

THE ECONOMIST

HEIRS

J.R.WILLIAMS

COMIN' AN' GOIN'.

OLD IRONSIDES

THE HIGH-HAT.

J.R.WILLIAMS

THE SLEEPER.

J.R.WILLIAMS

THE HAPPY FLOP.

J.R.WILLIAMS

THE QUEER GUY

PLAYIN' SAFE

THE FAMILY HEAD AND TAILS

114

THE OLD STALL

115

THE EMPTY FULL DAY

THE COVER-UP.

THE IDOL BUSTER.

120

THE FAT HEAD.

J.R.WILLIAMS

WORSE THAN ABSENT

J.R.WILLIAMS

THE LOST DAY.

J.R.WILLIAMS

A MAN APART.

J.R.WILLIAMS

THE STRUGGLER.

THE WANTER LUST.

127

"THE KING AWAITS"

J.R.WILLIAMS

SENDING HOME THE "BACON".

A ONE-MAN FIVE-PASSENGER.

131

THE PARTY OF THE THIRD PART.

THE CART AND THE HORSE.

J.R.WILLIAMS

THE AGONIZERS.

J.R.WILLIAMS

GOOD NEWS AND BAD.

THE TIME KILLER

J.R.WILLIAMS

ECONOMY

137

THE BUSYBODY

J.R.WILLIAMS

A LITTLE MISUNDERSTANDING.

AN OFF DAY.

J.R.WILLIAMS

MAKING A LONG STORY SHORT.

J.R.WILLIAMS

HEROES ARE MADE NOT BORN.

J.R.WILLIAMS

MAN OVER BOARD!

BUNKIES